the BaBy Book

THIS book is all about:

· ·

who was born on:

· · · · · · · · · · · · · · · ·

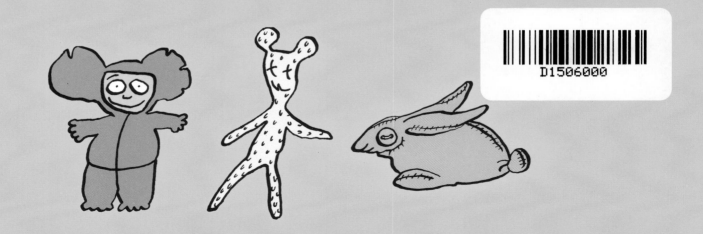

CONTENTS

Most baby books are as much fun as an exam at the dentist's about your tax form – and they make you feel guilty for not writing in them every week. But this one doesn't have any of those preposterous tasks like filling in 'The first time baby burped', 'Great-great-grandfather's hobbies and collar size' or 'The date the eleventh tooth appeared'. Instead, it lets you keep a record of the incidents and dates that are important for you and your family, and you can be as detailed or airy-fairy as you fancy.

You could start by applying the scientific method that I like to call 'Throwing Stuff Into a Box': use any old shoe box to hold photos, colour photocopies of cards, the kid's artwork and any other bits and pieces. And then, when you have time, pop them into *The Baby Book*. Each page of the book has suggestions about what can be recorded – which you can follow religiously, or completely ignore and stick a picture over.

You can write and glue something into the book every month or so, or keep the stuffed shoe box for a year before transferring your collection. If you have a lot of time (hollow laugh) you could decorate your memory box with the cards sent when your baby was born or had a birthday. Cards, letters, lists, notes and artwork can also be kept in the envelope at the back of *The Baby Book* (or those plastic spiral-bound books with see-through A4 pockets).

Remember to photocopy any faxes or ultrasound pictures because they'll eventually fade. And before you toss a photo into your shoe box, gently print the date and any other caption details on the back, so that when you come to put it in the book you'll have all the info you need.

You'll find a page in *The Baby Book* for jotting down immunisations and childhood illnesses: this is important info that your child may need, even decades later. It's amazing how many parents have no idea whether their grown-up children ever had chicken pox or allergic reactions when they were little.

Please don't worry about the book starting to look untidy and overly full – well, hey, it's supposed to represent a real life. Your grown-up baby is going to treasure this book forever. (But maybe don't give it to them until they're at least 30 or have their own children, in case it ends up being used as a coaster at a Mayonnaise-and-Beer-Throwing Loudest-Ever Funk Party.)

Have fun.

And go out and get some new shoes – after all, you're going to need the shoe box.

Kaz

Some ideas to try: record when Mum realised she was pregnant and how she felt, the due date, details of the pregnancy (like baby's first 'kicks' inside, Mum's food cravings, any health plans such as vitamins and exercise); include a photo of Dad (or Mum) recreating his facial expression when he heard about the baby on the way, pics of Mum with tum growing, photocopies of ultrasound images; jot down details of pre-parental hobbies, jobs, usual Saturday or week-night activities, an average weekly shopping list; put in some pics of parent(s) all dressed up for a big night out; list the names considered for boy and girl babies. What did the baby's room look like before you rejigged it for the new arrival?

Getting Ready

time capsule

Why not use these pages to create a 'time capsule' of the day/week/year your baby was born? You could include clippings of headline news stories; the name of the Prime Minister; the top five footy teams; lists from the newspapers or magazines of the most popular movies, songs and books; some pics from a fashion spread; ads from the paper; an average night from the TV guide; a pressed leaf or flower from your garden or nearest park; pics of the place where you live, your car or public transport, your telephone or a computer, hairstyles; food labels – anything your child will find quaint and interesting in thirty years' time.

first paparazzi shots:

These pages can evoke the Birth Day, by including lots of first photos of baby, family and friends, a list of the birth 'team' and any or all the details suggested on the opposite page (you could even add the weather forecast), a description of the labour, the comments from midwives and visitors when they saw the baby, a list of presents and visitors, samples of cards, a birth announcement from the newspaper or a private one sent to friends and family.

WELCOME to the WORLD

date & time:

weight:

length:

colour of eyes:

baldy or not:

birth team:

birth announcement:

@ HOME WITH a NEW BaBY

the FiRSt WeeKS

Create a mad montage to match your new life. Add a photo of you tired and still in your pyjamas during the day (compare it with the all-dressed-up photo a couple of pages back!), your weekly or daily routine (for example, feed for half an hour, play for an hour, sleep for four hours, look smug for having impossibly perfect baby all day long, repeat), a note on visitors and housework not done (why not photograph a mountainous pile of washing needing to be folded?); paste in your new weekly shopping list and a list or pic of things in the baby bag; record the first trip out in the pram, the reaction of any brothers or sisters to the new baby, your diary of breast or formula feeds; save pics of the baby's room, and the naming ceremony; write down who the baby looked like, week by week.

Have a go at the circular, non-traditional family 'sun' opposite. Once you paste in a photo of your baby, you can write in the name of anybody important around the circle, adding their relationship to the baby. Or, if you'd rather, paste in a more traditional family 'tree'. This page can be filled with pics of family and friends.

put pic of BABY
in the circle
& then arrange
family & friends'
names & relationship
to the baby all
around the
circle ...

Paternal grands, aunts & uncles, maternal grands

:dad

mum:

Cousins, special friends, brothers & sisters, etc

You can jot down sleep and nap routines at various ages, when the baby first slept through the night, moved during sleep, impersonated a wombat as a sleeping position; paste in photos of different jarmie outfits, the whole family in bed or the child asleep; record favourite night-time rituals, fluffy sleepy-time companions, sleepy stories at various ages, and toddler stalling tactics; tell tales of dummies, thumbsucking, and dreams; keep pics of the cot and bedroom.

Sleeping

Do the mashed potato:
keep pics and notes about the last
bottle or breast feeds, the first solid
foods eaten and crockery used
(this could include a pic of your
baby, in high chair, covered in
food), loved and hated foods for
baby/toddler/preschooler (pic of
screwed-up face?), family mealtimes,
favourite snacks, the toddler helping
to cook and the first solo chef
venture. Maybe write down a
favourite recipe for them to
recreate later in life.

Eating

It's normal for babies and toddlers to get sick while they're building up their immune system. Paste or write in the current schedule of required immunisations. You – and your child in adult life – will have an important record of which nasties they have been protected against. Also jot down the dates of any major infectious illnesses (such as chicken pox), allergic reactions or wheezing. You can record any antibiotics or other medicines taken, hospital visits or procedures, high fevers, ear infections, and hearing, eye and other tests. If you're keen on height and weight measurements, you can record them here too.

IMMUNISATION SCHEDULE*

Recommended age	Protects against	Date received

*The schedule is subject to change: check with your doctor for details about required vaccines.

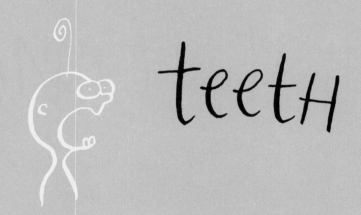

teeth

If you fancy it, keep a list of when teeth first appeared, and when the baby teeth fell out. Otherwise, use this page as a 0–7-year-old pics record of first teeth, toothbrush wielding, teeth that wobbled or fell out, a grin showing gaps in teeth, a mouth full of new teeth, and what the tooth fairy left beside the bed, in the glass or under the pillow.

19

BathTimes

Some ideas: pics of the baby in the little bath or sink (those early screaming pics can look like you're trying to boil the baby!), the toddler in the big bath, shared baths, bath toys and water games played, reactions to shampooing through the years, wet-hair sculptures, first shower.

CLOTHES

This is your gallery space for pics (or descriptions) of the first tiny outfits and booties, and favourite clothes through the years, and it's also a good place for pics of seasonal and party outfits, a hat parade, fancy dress, best clothes, new shoes and even haircuts.

You can go wild with pics of all the birthdays, cards, lists of guests, presents, games and food, copies of the invitations, year-by-year diagrams of the cake shapes, and a reminiscence about what drinking red lemonade does to small children.

BiRTHdayS

There are lots of celebrations every year so pick a few goodies from Christmas and other religious celebrations, Father's and Mother's Days and special days for your family. For example, Christmas could include a pic of your child on Santa's knee, a pic of the tree decorations, and a list of refreshments left out for the reindeer. For other celebrations, consider saving invitations, listing guests and presents, and describing the ceremonies performed, songs sung, things eaten and decorations.

CeleBRATIONS

Happy Holidays

HOLiDaYS & tRaveL

How about some pics of your holidays and travels, lists of what you packed, postcards sent and received. What travel games did you play? Who always won I Spy and why?

OutiNgS & OutDOORS

This is the place for remembering favourite or special outings to the zoo, the park, the beach, the bush, the corner shop. You can add pics, descriptions, your child's reactions and maybe a pressed leaf.

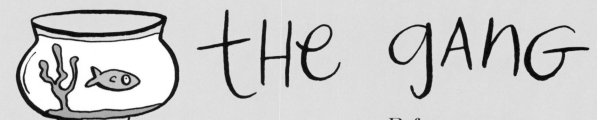

the gang

Before everyone changes forever, here's a spot to put pics of and stories about all the people, groups and animals that are really special during these first five years of your child's life: brothers and sisters, grandparents, cousins, aunts, close friends, carers, and pets or farm animals.

Bill

first Babysitters

29

toys

Maybe you'd like to keep memories of the favourite toys and furry (stuffed) friends at various ages: say, pics of a favourite old bear, your toddler stroking that fluffy scrap of fabric, toys that were terrible failures, the ones you couldn't leave behind when you went out, the contents of the toy box spread out, your child's first time on a bike. Also you can record things your child said about them.

games & pastimes

A spot for favourite games and pastimes at various ages. You can record them as descriptions, lists or pics of tree climbing, swimming, rainy-day pursuits, boardgames, sports, computer and digital games: all the way from peekaboo and banging saucepan lids and Ipsy Wipsy Spider through playing shops to dominoes and backyard cricket and strange dancing.

flies

31

BOOKS VIDEOS THEATRE TV FILMS etc.

Perhaps you could collect tickets from special plays, ads for favourite films, your child's 'reviews', miniature colour copies of book and video covers; mention the most requested books and loved TV characters; add pics of reading together or cultural outings.

radio

admit one

MuSiC

Keep a record of crucial lullabies on the sleepy-time tape or CD, nursery rhymes most enjoyed, special dancing music, favourite lyric fragments, musical instruments played, and first songs requested, learned off by heart and sung most often.

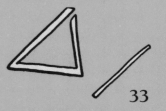

This is the place for words, sentences, sayings, explanations, and lyrics invented or enjoyed. Jot down weird babbles, first words, mispronunciations, brilliant observations, made-up words, first words and sentences, terrible attempts at jokes, repeated questions, and words that tickled their fancy or yours.

TALKING

There's room here for pics of typical facial expressions or actions, a record of parents' feelings or thoughts on the child's characteristics and personality, and perhaps a gallery of crying, laughing, frowning, shouting and sleeping pics.

typical

No o o o o o

1 2 3 4 5 6 7 8 9 0

You can collect examples of the first time scribbles almost
turned into letters of the alphabet, an early backwards signature, the first letter
or postcard written, kisses written down: anything really from first scribbles to
first sentences and stories. You might like to jot down the date on each one.

a b c d e f g h i j k l m n

WRITINGS

opq Rst uvw xyz

Paste in first pencil and crayon drawings, first paintings, special pictures with your child's dictated captions ('It's a rocket!'), the first face and whole person drawn. You can also use this space for pics of your child in a smock, doing footprints, taking part in craft activities, or with face paint on.

Art

art

You could record the inaugural smile, grasp, grab, clap, solo sit-up, roll over, dragging of the bum along the floor, crawl, kiss, wave, ice-cream, haircut (you can tape in some hair), pulling self up onto furniture, step, walk, ballistic bawl, babble, hum, laugh. Photos don't have to be of literally the first time something is done, and if you don't know the exact time and date just write something like 'at about 10 months'.

Baby 'firsts' & favourites

toddler 'firsts' & favourites

How about the first day at play group, baby gym or child-care centre (this may belong on an earlier page, of course!), real day without nappies (this could well happen after 3 years, though), the first time your child runs, catches, has a tantrum, throws, tries to explain something, puts on own hat, builds (and knocks down) a tower of blocks, uses a fork and spoon, has dinner without the high chair, draws a recognisable face.

48

Space to remember swims, hops, dancing lessons, solo getting-dressed mission, day at a sporting event, being taught to catch a ball or ride a bike, building a cubby, getting a pet, a day at creche, child-care, preschool or kinder, seeing the ocean, the bush, a waterfall, a concert performance, making a necklace, hammering in a nail . . .

PreSchool 'firsts' & favourites

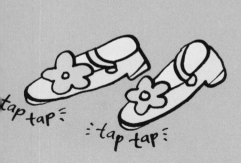

tap tap
tap tap

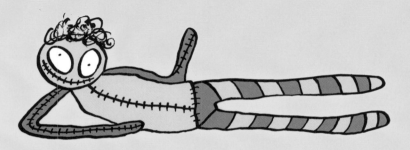

These pages are for anything extra – and maybe a photo of your 'baby' in school clothes.